My
Hiking
Journal

*My personal journal for recording
and celebrating memorable experiences
on my adventures in Nature.*

Julia L Wright

HieroGraphics Books, LLC

www.HieroGraphicsBooksLLC.com

Published by HieroGraphics Books, LLC
First Printing, October 2016

Printed in the United States of America

HieroGraphics Books, LLC
106 Ruxton Ave
Manitou Springs, CO 80829

ISBN-13: 978-0996581608
ISBN-10: 099658160X

My
Hiking
Journal

*My personal journal for recording
and celebrating memorable experiences
on my adventures in Nature.*

Contact Information:

_____

_____

_____

_____

_____

_____

All who wander are not lost.
J. R. R. Tolkien

This Hiking
Journal
Belongs To:

Related Books from HieroGraphics Books

Trails Guide to Front Range Colorado: Denver to Pikes Peak
Zoltan Malocsay

My Camping Adventures Journal by Julia L. Wright

My 30 Week Gratitude Journal by Julia L. Wright

Monthly Dream Journal by Julia L. Wright

How To Plan A Sustainable Event by Julia L. Wright

Discover Essential Oils for Optimum Health by Julia L. Wright

Discover the World of Squirrels by Violet Burbach

Handbook To Health
by Vivian Rice and Edie Wogaman, revised and edited by Julia L. Wright

Galloping Wind: The Legend of Wild Shadow,
The Wind-That-Gallops by Zoltan Malocsay

Where Do I Belong? by Susan Grace

Sinister Frog: A Radio Show for Twisted Minds
By Bob Kelsey

Natural Health Book Series Based on
Orison Swett Marden's *"Cheerfulness As A Life Power"*
Available on Kindle, Revised and enhanced by Julia L Wright

Book 1: Laughter and Essential Oils: Natural Cures for Dis-Ease
Book 2: Optimism and Essential Oils: Natural Cures for Depression
Book 3: Positive Attitude and Essential Oils: Natural Ways to Alleviate Stress
Book 4: Cheerfulness and Essential Oils: Natural Ways to Create a Joyful Life
Book 5: Giving and Essential Oils: Naturally Create the Life You Desire
Book 6: A Sunny Nature and Essential Oils: Naturally Create Optimum Health

As A Man Thinketh
James Allen - revised and enhanced by Julia L. Wright

To see what other informative or activity books, art prints, calendars or journals are available from Hierographics Books at:www.HieroGraphicsBooksLLC.com

Being prepared and understanding the best ways to stay safe can make the difference between having an enjoyable or a challenging, perhaps disastrous, hiking experience. This informative FREE brochure includes many tips on how you can be best prepared to stay safe on your hiking adventures. Sign up to download:
My Hiking Journal Bonus "Tips for Hiking Safely", at:
www.hierographicsbooksllc.com/hiking-journal-safely/

These tips will help you discover the right steps to take to safely experience your hiking excursions into Nature.

Included in this FREE pdf bonus file are some color images of trails around Colorado and other Western States to inspire you to get out in Nature and start hiking on a regular basis.

Discover beautiful Colorado hiking trails at:
http://www.spiritrenewinghikes.com/

Look deep into nature, then you will understand everything better.
~ Albert Einstein~

Let every step you take upon the earth be as a prayer.
~ Black Elk ~

Table of Contents

Treat the Earth well.
It was not given to you by your parents,
it was loaned to you by your children.
We do not inherit the Earth from our Ancestors,
we borrow it from our Children.
~ Ancient Indian Proverb ~

And while I stood there I saw more than I can tell,
and I understood more than I saw;
for I was seeing in a sacred manner the shapes of things in the spirit,
and the shape of all shapes as they must live together like one being.
~ Black Elk ~

Introduction To Your Hiking Journal

Years ago, journals were a common place item in people's homes. Keeping a journal to chronical personal experiences has declined over time. But recently there has been a resurgence in the use of journaling for many reasons.

There are many benefits of having a hiking journal. Keeping a hiking journal allows you to keep track of the places you visited with notes about why you would like to return there. Writing in a hiking journal will help you to remember specific routes you took when faced with forks in a trail. It will help you keep track of the places you visited, sights you saw and the miles you hiked.

It is a great tool to use to look back on some of the hikes that you have taken. You can use it to remind yourself of the beauty you saw on each trail and memories of wonderful times spent with friends. By jotting down notes about your thoughts that were inspired by each hike, you will be able to find more joy in your day-to-day world.

Writing in a hiking journal makes your time in Nature seem timeless and unforgettable.

The information you can record in this journal includes:
- Hike Date
- Trail Name
- Trail Location
- Hiking Companions
- Directions to Trailhead
- How much time it took to get there
- Portalets in parking area?
- Are dogs allowed?
- Trail Length
- Trail Difficulty
- How far I hiked
- Time hike started and ended
- Time spent hiking
- Stopped for lunch *(Can add the food you brought.)*
- Weather
- What I liked best about the trail
- What I liked least about the hike
- Camped overnight *(If you don't camp, make up own heading.)*
- What are my goals for this hike?

Just as a plucked string can cause another string to vibrate, we can begin to resonate in harmony with natural beauty by studying and appreciating it. By exposing ourselves to the wonders of nature, we can foster an internal harmony that benefits every aspect of our being.
~ Thomas Ashley-Farrand ~

- Insights I had while hiking *(Or write a poem or very short story.)*
- I saw these types of birds, creatures, flowers, insects
- I took photos of
- Was the trail well-marked?
- Were there many side trails?
- More notes about the Trail

These types of notes are especially helpful when planning your next hike. And they can be very useful when planning what you might want to change if you want to return to a specific trail in the future, or if you want to share your insights about the trail with a friend.

There are 52 sets of double pages where you can write about each of your hikes in this journal. This means you can track a full year of weekly hikes or 52 hikes you take over a longer span of time.

After a series of hikes, there are a couple of pages to write about some of the most memorable experiences you had and reflect upon what insights you had during your most recent hikes. Or you can use these pages to write a poem, a very short story or compose a song that any hike inspired.

This journal has a few pages at the back to note places you would like to visit in the future. After you hike any of those trails, you can note the pages you wrote about hikes. This will help remind yourself how much you enjoyed it and where you might want to go on a future visit.

If you want to share places you loved hiking with others, this journal can be used as an easy reference to share hints about the reason you enjoyed a specific hike and any difficulties you encountered on your hike.

Having good directions to where each trail begins in writing will be helpful when giving them directions for how to find a particular trailhead and how long it will take to get there.

And, if you should ever find yourself feeling down in the future you can look back at these pages to remind yourself of all the places you hiked and the beauty you experienced that gave you pleasure on those glorious days spent out in nature, and inspire you to get out in Nature once again, be it for a short local hike or a far away adventure.

Be sure to read the section entitled *Things To Know Before You Go* to ensure a better understanding of how to safely hike.

For more information about staying safe when hiking, download the free PDF bonus *Tips for Hiking Safely* to be better prepared for all you hiking adventures.

Origin of the word hike

Early 19th century *(originally dialect, as a verb)* of unknown origin around 1800-1810.

Dictionary Definitions

hiking
verb (used without object), hiked, hiking.

1. To go on an extended walk for pleasure or exercise, especially in a natural setting.

2. To travel over on foot for pleasure or exercise.

3. To walk or march a great distance, especially through rural areas, for pleasure, exercise, military training, or the like.

4. Walk for a long distance, especially across country or in the woods.

hiking
noun
The sporting or leisure activity of going for long, often strenuous, walks in the country.

hike
noun

1. A long walk or march.

2. A long walk or march for recreational activity, military training, or the like.

Synonyms: walk, trek, tramp, tromp, trudge, slog, march; ramble, rove, traipse.

Defining Hiking

It doesn't matter where you live, there are beautiful places you can discover to get out and hike in. There are plenty of wild areas to explore no matter where on this beautiful planet you live.

Though most people define *hiking* as getting out into a wilderness area that is a bit more challenging than your everyday walk around the block, *hiking* doesn't necessarily have to imply doing something challenging, nor do you have to travel great distances to find a path or trail to hike upon. You can take a hike by meandering along a path in a local park or following a river walk as well as exploring a trail deep in a wilderness area. Hiking should be a pleasurable past-time that you want to do many times all year round.

The most basic concept of *hiking* that anyone can experience is to get out into an area of Nature and start walking with eyes wide open to the beauty the natural world offers to you to enjoy.

People often hike as a way to enjoy exercising. Others just want to experience a peaceful time in Nature. Some people chose to hike in order to contemplate Spiritual questions by being in solitude away from civilization, or to have a clear connection with their higher self or guides. Whatever your purpose for hiking may be, make your plans and get moving.

There are people who do enjoy short walks, while others think it must be an all day adventure and strenuous. However long and challenging you want your hike to be, is your choice. The length and type of hike you wish to embark upon will determine where and how often you chose to hike.

A *day hike* is probably the most common form of hiking people chose to take. It allows them to get out in Nature and be some place where they can escape from their everyday chores and challenges.

Spending time surrounded by Nature helps clear the mind and uplifts the Spirit in many ways, and your body will thank you by becoming stronger when you get it out and moving.

If you enjoy camping, this adds another dimension for hiking opportunities. Often people will choose a camp site that is near the trailhead of a day long hike they wish to explore. Being able to savor the experience of a long hike without having to jump back in the a car and drive back into civilization can enhance the benefits of hiking on many levels. Having a camp site set-up and welcoming you when returning from a long hike makes it possible to return to a restful

With beauty before me, may I walk.
With beauty behind me, may I walk.
With beauty above me, may I walk.
With beauty all around me, may I walk.
Wandering on a trail of beauty; lively may I walk.
~ Navajo Prayer ~

place to relax and savor the experience. Camping after a long hike avoids the stress of having to drive back in traffic to your home where you would be immediately immersed in your everyday world.

Backpacking on trails is another way to take long hikes that usually are pretty strenuous, but can take you to places that fewer people will ever get to see and enjoy.

The safest way to take a hike is on an established trail. People do decide to follow their own routes and *bushwhack* into unmarked territory. This is not safe or good for the environment. Think twice, and then think again before going off-trail. Are you prepared to find your way back? What is calling to you to do this? So many trails take you into awesome spaces, bushwhacking into unknown territory is not necessary to have a wonderful hiking experience.

You can hike unencumbered or with a full pack, depending upon where and how long you wish to hike. *Though carrying a bottle of water is suggested for any hike. Staying hydrated is important when doing any type of exercise.*

It is best to go hiking with at least one companion or in a group. Some people hike with their dogs. If you do choose to hike alone in a wilderness area, be sure someone knows where you plan to hike.

Whichever style of hike you take, a little bit of planning goes a long way to making it safe and thoroughly enjoyable.

As you become more comfortable with hiking it will become more and more enjoyable. This will create a desire to get out in Nature as often as possible, and it will soon become a habit to take time to hike.

May the Warm Winds of Heaven
Blow softly upon your house.
May the Great Spirit
Bless all who enter there.
May your Moccasins
Make happy tracks
in many snows,
and may the Rainbow
Always touch your shoulder.
  ~ Cherokee Prayer Blessing ~

Creating The Habit Of Hiking

Taking a hike is a great way to get in touch with a slower pace of life that is missing in our modern world. You will enjoy endless new experiences while on a hike. Writing about these experiences in a journal makes them timeless. And if you are a writer, artist, musician or painter, they can inspire ideas to use to enhance your way of interpreting the world and sharing it with your various audiences.

You can decide to hike once a week, every other week, once a month or some other time frame that works for you. You can chose to do hikes that are simple and nearby or farther away, or mix them up.

Perhaps you want to hike in one area many times during different seasons or explore a new trail or path every time you go hiking. Setting a goal to get out and hike is important to get yourself into the *habit of hiking* and enjoying Nature.

Most hikes into wilderness areas require a person to drive or take a bike to access a trailhead. So people are often surprised at the number of places in or nearby the urban areas they live where they can easily access a trail to hike.

Only you can determine what best fits into your schedule and that you can physically handle. You need to set goals relating to which hikes you want to take in the future. But if you don't do the research and make plans by scheduling them in advance and in ways that allow you to reach those goals, you will find yourself taking the easy way out and saying, *"Next week I'll go"* and lose the opportunity to hike as planned. That is why there is a section at the end of this journal to list hikes you would like to take.

It is best to start hiking with the attitude that you will be wandering through a magical land. Choose a hike that matches your abilities. Don't try to walk really fast just to get to the end of a trail. You will miss so much of the beauty if you don't take time to meander and stop to look around you at all that Nature has to offer. Take time to sit on a log or a rock or on the ground and listen to the sounds made by wind blowing through the leaves in the trees and birds calling to each other.

Although there is no dearth of trails to discover and walk upon to create a habit of hiking, it will require a bit of research to discover the ones located close by. The research can be very fun. Set aside time to discover places you think you will enjoy hiking in near your home or on a vacation. Ask friends who hike which trails they most

Sometimes, I need to go off on my own.
I'm not sad, I'm not angry.
I'm just recharging my batteries.
~ Sprit Science ~

The unexplainable thing in nature that makes me feel the world is
big fat beyond my understanding — to understand maybe by trying
to put it into form. To find the feeling of infinity on the horizon line
or just over the next hill.
~ Georgia O'Keeffe ~

enjoy. They may offer to take you with them on one of their next adventures to get you started.

And if you just find one place nearby, get up, get out and go exploring. Once you find out how enjoyable that first hike is, you will be hooked! It will inspire you to search farther for the next adventure, or to return to the same trail and discover the changes in the fauna or flora and many other things you did not see on your first visit.

Many books can be found that describe trails in areas all around the United States and the world. Do some research for books online or walk into your favorite local bookstore or outdoor equipment store and purchase one that focuses on the areas you would like to explore near and far.

Searching on the Internet will reveal many groups or individuals that share their favorite hiking trails all around the world and ways to find them. You may be able to find a group on Meet-Up that hikes in your area that will welcome a new member. Photographs that groups or individuals post online taken on their various hikes will surely entice you to explore nearby places you never knew existed.

You will want to carry this journal with you. Logging the times and distances is much easier when you arrive at your destination or finish the traveling part of a trip than trying to remember them later.

This journal has space to write your thoughts about each hike you take. When you have time to take a break on a trail, pull it out and write in some observations. Don't leave it up to the idea that *"I will remember this when I get home."* Chances are you won't. But if you don't get everything written during the hike, or as a passenger on the ride home, don't let too much time pass before you fill in the blanks or you will most likely forget much of what you did and saw that day.

When this journal is filled, don't stop there. Be sure you have another one on hand to continue on your path of exploring the world in a healthy, adventurous, exciting and joy-filled way that will give you a new understanding of why you are here.

You need regular doses of unreasonable beauty, sublime anomalies,
beguiling ephemera, and inexplicable joys.
~ Rob Brezsny ~

In every walk with nature one receives far more than he seeks.
~ John Muir, American environmentalist ~

Things To Consider Before You Go Hiking

The world is filled with natural beauty anywhere you live. Trails exist to allow you to explore every type of landscape imaginable. But first you need to find them and make the proper preparations to have a safe and enjoyable hike.

Taking a hike in a distant wilderness area involves more risks than hiking a trail in a more urban setting. But all trails can involve some elements of risk. Making sure you are properly prepared is absolutely your responsibility.

Take time to research information that others have shared about a trail you are considering hiking. This will help to make sure you know the difficulty of a trail, how long a trail is, if it is a loop or an in-and-back-out route, the type of terrain you will be hiking and how much elevation gain you will experience.

Getting good directions to a trailhead is essential. Knowing where a trail begins and the nearest parking options for easy access to it will save lots of time when going to a remote location.

Sometimes people think having an *"app"* on a phone to guide them to the trailhead will suffice, but remember internet access in wilderness areas can be very spotty. Having a map or a great guidebook to get you to your destination is very useful when a phone says *"No Service"* and you haven't reached the Trailhead. *There is perhaps nothing more frustrating than driving out to the place you thought a trail began and getting lost on a dirt road, taking precious time away from your hiking.*

Always be sure you have your identification, including contact and insurance information, with you in a written form.

Rules of use vary depending on the type of trail you will be accessing. Make sure you check the regulations relating to allowing dogs or times a trail may be closed due to weather or wildlife mating times.

Understanding the type of uses a trail allows can help you to be aware you may encounter horses, all-terrain vehicles or cyclists on trails that allow multi-use options.

Another bit of preparation you will want to do in order to ensure your time hiking is enjoyable and safe is to look into equipment you might want to have. Having the right shoes and pack can make all the difference in the world between being miserable or totally comfortable when hiking on different types of trails. If you are a beginning hiker, get advice from friends who hike. Go shopping at a store that has

Thus shall ye look on all this fleeting world:
A star at dawn, a bubble in the stream,
A flash of lightning in a summer cloud,
A flickering lamp, a phantom, and a dream.
~ The Buddha ~

knowledgeable salespeople to get you into the proper type of shoes, clothing and a pack that is comfortable. Always test wearing new shoes on short walks before setting off on wilderness hike.

For short hikes, many people just use a fanny pack that holds water and a few other essentials and maybe a bit of food.

But when you head out into a wilderness area or on a long hike, you will want to have a day or full-size backpack. This means filling a pack with a variety of items. Be sure to include some first aid items, easy to eat trail food, maps, extra clothes, and a way to carry plenty of water. A rain poncho comes in handy to protect you not just from rain, but cold winds. A couple of extra things to add are a whistle, a compass and a flashlight in case you misjudge your timing and end up out in the dark on a trail or get lost.

There are many other items that can help a person find their way if they get lost. Ask at your local outdoor sport store for suggestions if you plan on taking long hikes in wilderness areas.

Many books and web sites exist that have more detailed information about equipment you need to have on any type of hike. Check out the list of items deemed essential for even short day-hikes in a trail book, on web sites and download the free bonus pdf, *Tips for Hiking Safely,* to learn more and be better prepared for hiking.

Any good outdoor equipment supply store is likely to have knowledgeable salespeople who can help you best determine what you need to be comfortable and well-equipped for the type of hikes you plan on taking. Ask questions and try on different shoes, packs, jackets to find ones that suit you body and hiking needs.

Comfortable shoes are very important to ensure you enjoy your hiking experience. When hiking wilderness trails, good boots with support for your ankles, not sneakers, are a must have!

It is important to carry lots of water to stay hydrated when hiking. Never, ever drink water from a stream or lake. Dangerous parasites abound in these innocent and inviting looking sources of water.

Many people like to hike with one or two walking poles. This gives them a sense of balance and can be very helpful when hiking on lose gravel or on a narrow trail. Other people get along fine without poles.

When choosing a place to hike, you will want to be sure you choose a trail that is not too far out of your comfort zone. Steep hills can be a challenge for even the most practiced hiker. When you find yourself gasping for breath, it is time to stop and look around. Take some deep breaths, relax and enjoy your surroundings.

To truly know the world, look deeply within your own being;
to truly know yourself, take real interest in the world.
~ Rudolf Steiner ~

If you listen carefully enough to anything,
it will talk to you.
~ George Washington Carver ~

If a trail starts by going uphill and keeps climbing up, it is pretty safe to assume you will have enough energy to hike back out no matter how far you hike. Since you will be walking downhill most of the way you will get back out much quicker than the time it took you to hike to the place where you decide to turn around.

But when a trail goes downhill at its beginning, the going in seems easy and this may tempt you to hike farther than is safe for your ability to climb back up those hills to get back to the car. It will take you at least twice the time to get back out than it took you to get in going downhill most of the way. Consider how long you want to hike in such a situation and make sure you stop at a point that will allow you to hike uphill and out.

There are many subtle points of trail etiquette to learn beyond what is mentioned in the following paragraphs.

One of the most important rules to remember in order that a trail can be maintained and enjoyed by others who come after you is to have *minimum impact* on the area. This means that you must pack out anything you brought in with you. Empty items are much lighter than the full ones you brought. Burying garbage means an animal will come dig it up. If you leave it near a stream, it can get washed into the water and add to pollution that will be carried downstream.

Many people do not realize that it is not legal to pick or dig up wildflowers, moss or any other plants. It is really sad to see that people carve their initials into living trees. This can harm them and changes their natural beauty.

One of the most distressing recent trends has been people spray painting on rocks. Nature does not need to be enhanced with artificial colors! No matter how great an artist someone might consider himself or herself to be, natural formations should never to be used as a *"canvas"* for anyone's *"artistic"* endeavors. Defacing natural formations and rocks is punishable by law everywhere.

Although many people don't totally understand the reason for these rules, by leaving Nature as it is presented to you in its natural state, you ensure that the next person who comes along a trail will have the same beautiful experience you have enjoyed.

You will also want to be respectful to others in your party or those you meet on a trail. Most people are hiking to find a quiet space and so shouting loudly among yourselves or playing music is not respectful of others in a wilderness area.

Embody the three harmonies:
within
with other;
and with nature.
~ Robert Gilman ~

Smile, breathe and go slowly
~ Thich Nhat Hanh ~

Don't toss rocks off the side of a trail, as someone could be down below and become injured.

Faster groups and horses have the right-of-way on every trail. Move off to the side, preferably the downhill side and let them pass. Bicyclists are suppose to yield to hikers, but their speed when going downhill often makes that difficult. If you hear them coming, it is best to take a step to the side of a trail and let them pass.

If you encounter someone who asks a question about the trail, take a moment and give them an informed answer if you do have knowledge that can help them better enjoy their hiking experience.

Most trail guide books have lots of information regarding how to hike with dogs, what to do if you meet lions or bears and so many other helpful hints on how to hike safely. Make sure you read about sanitation in the wilderness and how to handle your bodily waste, as you won't find restrooms along any trail.

Take the time to learn ways to stay safe when hiking before you set off on your first hike and all subsequent hikes.

The free bonus pdf *Tips for Hiking Safely* offered on our web site has many details to help you prepare for safe hiking.

By being prepared on all levels, you will discover that hiking is a most enjoyable and rewarding experience.

So are you ready and excited to start your hiking journal?

It begins on the next page!

Stay safe and have amazing and fun adventures!

There are only two ways to live your life.
One is as though nothing is a miracle.
The other is as though everything is a miracle.
~ Albert Einstein~

Hike Date: _____

Trail Name: _____

Trail Location: _____

Hiking Companions: _____

_____

Distance and Directions to Trailhead: _____

_____

_____

_____

_____

_____

How much time it took to get there: _____

Portalet in parking area: Yes _____ **No** _____ **Seasonal** _____

Are dogs allowed: Yes _____ **No** _____

Trail Length: _____ **Trail Difficulty:** _____

How far I hiked: _____

Time: Hike Started: _____ **Time: Hike Ended:** _____

Time spent hiking: _____

Stopped for lunch: _____

Weather: _____

What I liked best: _____

What I liked least: _____

Camped overnight or longer: _____

_____

_____

What are my goals for this hike?

_____

_____

_____

Insights I had while hiking:

_____

_____

_____

_____

_____

I saw these types of birds, creatures, flowers, insects:

_____

_____

_____

I took photos of:

_____

_____

_____

_____

Was the trail well marked?

Were there many side trails?

More notes about the Trail:

_____

_____

_____

_____

_____

_____

Hike Date: _____

Trail Name: _____

Trail Location: _____

Hiking Companions: _____

_____

_____

Distance and Directions to Trailhead: _____

_____

_____

_____

_____

_____

_____

How much time it took to get there: _____

Portalet in parking area: Yes _____ **No** _____ **Seasonal** _____

Are dogs allowed: Yes _____ **No** _____

Trail Length: _____ **Trail Difficulty:** _____

How far I hiked: _____

Time: Hike Started: _____ **Time: Hike Ended:** _____

Time spent hiking: _____

Stopped for lunch: _____

Weather: _____

What I liked best: _____

What I liked least: _____

Camped overnight or longer: _____

_____

_____

_____

What are my goals for this hike?

Insights I had while hiking:

I saw these types of birds, creatures, flowers, insects:

I took photos of:

Was the trail well marked?

Were there many side trails?

More notes about the Trail:

Hike Date: _____

Trail Name: _____

Trail Location: _____

Hiking Companions: _____

_____

Distance and Directions to Trailhead: _____

_____

_____

_____

_____

_____

How much time it took to get there: _____

Portalet in parking area: Yes ____ **No** ____ **Seasonal** ____

Are dogs allowed: Yes ____ **No** ____

Trail Length: ____ **Trail Difficulty:** ____

How far I hiked: _____

Time: Hike Started: ____ **Time: Hike Ended:** ____

Time spent hiking: _____

Stopped for lunch: _____

Weather: _____

What I liked best: _____

_____

What I liked least: _____

_____

Camped overnight or longer: _____

_____

_____

_____

What are my goals for this hike? _____

_____

_____

_____

Insights I had while hiking: _____

_____

_____

_____

_____

_____

I saw these types of birds, creatures, flowers, insects:

_____

_____

_____

I took photos of: _____

_____

_____

_____

_____

_____

Was the trail well marked? _____

Were there many side trails? _____

More notes about the Trail: _____

_____

_____

_____

_____

_____

_____

_____

Hike Date: ....

Trail Name: ....

Trail Location: ....

Hiking Companions: ....

....

Distance and Directions to Trailhead: ....

....

....

....

....

....

....

How much time it took to get there: ....

Portalet in parking area: Yes ...... **No** ...... **Seasonal** ....

Are dogs allowed: Yes ...... **No** ......

Trail Length: .... **Trail Difficulty:** ....

How far I hiked: ....

Time: Hike Started: .... **Time: Hike Ended:** ....

Time spent hiking: ....

Stopped for lunch: ....

Weather: ....

What I liked best: ....

....

What I liked least: ....

....

Camped overnight or longer: ....

....

....

....

What are my goals for this hike?

Insights I had while hiking:

I saw these types of birds, creatures, flowers, insects:

I took photos of:

Was the trail well marked?

Were there many side trails?

More notes about the Trail:

Hike Date: _____

Trail Name: _____

Trail Location: _____

Hiking Companions: _____

_____

_____

Distance and Directions to Trailhead: _____

_____

_____

_____

_____

_____

_____

How much time it took to get there: _____

Portalet in parking area: Yes ____ **No** ____ **Seasonal** _____

Are dogs allowed: Yes ____ **No** _____

Trail Length: _____ **Trail Difficulty:** _____

How far I hiked: _____

Time: Hike Started: _____ **Time: Hike Ended:** _____

Time spent hiking: _____

Stopped for lunch: _____

Weather: _____

What I liked best: _____

_____

What I liked least: _____

_____

Camped overnight or longer: _____

_____

_____

What are my goals for this hike?

Insights I had while hiking:

I saw these types of birds, creatures, flowers, insects:

I took photos of:

Was the trail well marked?

Were there many side trails?

More notes about the Trail:

32

Hike Date: _____

Trail Name: _____

Trail Location: _____

Hiking Companions: _____

_____

_____

Distance and Directions to Trailhead: _____

_____

_____

_____

_____

_____

How much time it took to get there: _____

Portalet in parking area: Yes _____ **No** _____ **Seasonal** _____

Are dogs allowed: Yes _____ **No** _____

Trail Length: _____ **Trail Difficulty:** _____

How far I hiked: _____

Time: Hike Started: _____ **Time: Hike Ended:** _____

Time spent hiking: _____

Stopped for lunch: _____

Weather: _____

What I liked best: _____

What I liked least: _____

Camped overnight or longer: _____

_____

_____

What are my goals for this hike?

Insights I had while hiking:

I saw these types of birds, creatures, flowers, insects:

I took photos of:

Was the trail well marked?

Were there many side trails?

More notes about the Trail:

Describe Your Most Memorable Hiking Experiences.

What insights has hiking given you?

Hike Date: ....

Trail Name: ....

Trail Location: ....

Hiking Companions: ....

....

....

Distance and Directions to Trailhead: ....

....

....

....

....

....

How much time it took to get there: ....

Portalet in parking area: Yes .... **No** .... **Seasonal** ....

Are dogs allowed: Yes .... **No** ....

Trail Length: .... **Trail Difficulty:** ....

How far I hiked: ....

Time: Hike Started: .... **Time: Hike Ended:** ....

Time spent hiking: ....

Stopped for lunch: ....

Weather: ....

What I liked best: ....

What I liked least: ....

Camped overnight or longer: ....

....

....

What are my goals for this hike? _____

_____

_____

_____

Insights I had while hiking: _____

_____

_____

_____

_____

_____

I saw these types of birds, creatures, flowers, insects: _____

_____

_____

_____

I took photos of: _____

_____

_____

_____

_____

_____

Was the trail well marked? _____

Were there many side trails? _____

More notes about the Trail: _____

_____

_____

_____

_____

_____

_____

Hike Date: _____

Trail Name: _____

Trail Location: _____

Hiking Companions: _____

_____

_____

Distance and Directions to Trailhead: _____

_____

_____

_____

_____

_____

_____

How much time it took to get there: _____

Portalet in parking area: Yes ____ **No** ____ **Seasonal** _____

Are dogs allowed: Yes ____ **No** ____

Trail Length: _____ **Trail Difficulty:** _____

How far I hiked: _____

Time: Hike Started: _____ **Time: Hike Ended:** _____

Time spent hiking: _____

Stopped for lunch: _____

Weather: _____

What I liked best: _____

_____

What I liked least: _____

_____

Camped overnight or longer: _____

_____

_____

_____

What are my goals for this hike?

Insights I had while hiking:

I saw these types of birds, creatures, flowers, insects:

I took photos of:

Was the trail well marked?

Were there many side trails?

More notes about the Trail:

Hike Date: _____

Trail Name: _____

Trail Location: _____

Hiking Companions: _____

_____

Distance and Directions to Trailhead: _____

_____

_____

_____

_____

_____

_____

How much time it took to get there: _____

Portalet in parking area: Yes _____ **No** _____ **Seasonal** _____

Are dogs allowed: Yes _____ **No** _____

Trail Length: _____ **Trail Difficulty:** _____

How far I hiked: _____

Time: Hike Started: _____ **Time: Hike Ended:** _____

Time spent hiking: _____

Stopped for lunch: _____

Weather: _____

What I liked best: _____

What I liked least: _____

Camped overnight or longer: _____

_____

_____

What are my goals for this hike? _____

_____

_____

Insights I had while hiking: _____

_____

_____

_____

_____

I saw these types of birds, creatures, flowers, insects:

_____

_____

I took photos of: _____

_____

_____

_____

_____

Was the trail well marked? _____

Were there many side trails? _____

More notes about the Trail: _____

_____

_____

_____

_____

_____

_____

Hike Date: _____

Trail Name: _____

Trail Location: _____

Hiking Companions: _____

_____

Distance and Directions to Trailhead: _____

_____

_____

_____

_____

_____

_____

How much time it took to get there: _____

Portalet in parking area: Yes _____ **No** _____ **Seasonal** _____

Are dogs allowed: Yes _____ **No** _____

Trail Length: _____ **Trail Difficulty:** _____

How far I hiked: _____

Time: Hike Started: _____ **Time: Hike Ended:** _____

Time spent hiking: _____

Stopped for lunch: _____

Weather: _____

What I liked best: _____

What I liked least: _____

Camped overnight or longer: _____

_____

_____

What are my goals for this hike?

Insights I had while hiking:

I saw these types of birds, creatures, flowers, insects:

I took photos of:

Was the trail well marked?

Were there many side trails?

More notes about the Trail:

Hike Date: _____

Trail Name: _____

Trail Location: _____

Hiking Companions: _____

_____

Distance and Directions to Trailhead: _____

_____

_____

_____

_____

_____

How much time it took to get there: _____

Portalet in parking area: Yes _____ **No** _____ **Seasonal** _____

Are dogs allowed: Yes _____ **No** _____

Trail Length: _____ **Trail Difficulty:** _____

How far I hiked: _____

Time: Hike Started: _____ **Time: Hike Ended:** _____

Time spent hiking: _____

Stopped for lunch: _____

_____

Weather: _____

What I liked best: _____

_____

What I liked least: _____

_____

Camped overnight or longer: _____

_____

_____

_____

What are my goals for this hike? _____

_____

_____

_____

Insights I had while hiking: _____

_____

_____

_____

_____

_____

I saw these types of birds, creatures, flowers, insects: _____

_____

_____

_____

I took photos of: _____

_____

_____

_____

_____

Was the trail well marked? _____

Were there many side trails? _____

More notes about the Trail: _____

_____

_____

_____

_____

_____

_____

_____

Hike Date: _____

Trail Name: _____

Trail Location: _____

Hiking Companions: _____

_____

_____

Distance and Directions to Trailhead: _____

_____

_____

_____

_____

_____

_____

How much time it took to get there: _____

Portalet in parking area: Yes _____ **No** _____ **Seasonal** _____

Are dogs allowed: Yes _____ **No** _____

Trail Length: _____ **Trail Difficulty:** _____

How far I hiked: _____

Time: Hike Started: _____ **Time: Hike Ended:** _____

Time spent hiking: _____

Stopped for lunch: _____

_____

Weather: _____

What I liked best: _____

_____

What I liked least: _____

_____

Camped overnight or longer: _____

_____

_____

What are my goals for this hike?

Insights I had while hiking:

I saw these types of birds, creatures, flowers, insects:

I took photos of:

Was the trail well marked?

Were there many side trails?

More notes about the Trail:

Hike Date: ....

Trail Name: ....

Trail Location: ....

Hiking Companions: ....

....

....

Distance and Directions to Trailhead: ....

....

....

....

....

....

....

How much time it took to get there: ....

Portalet in parking area: Yes .... **No** .... **Seasonal** ....

Are dogs allowed: Yes .... **No** ....

Trail Length: .... **Trail Difficulty:** ....

How far I hiked: ....

Time: Hike Started: .... **Time: Hike Ended:** ....

Time spent hiking: ....

Stopped for lunch: ....

Weather: ....

What I liked best: ....

....

What I liked least: ....

....

Camped overnight or longer: ....

....

....

What are my goals for this hike?

Insights I had while hiking:

I saw these types of birds, creatures, flowers, insects:

I took photos of:

Was the trail well marked?

Were there many side trails?

More notes about the Trail:

Describe Your Most Memorable Hiking Experiences

What insights has hiking given you?

Hike Date: _____

Trail Name: _____

Trail Location: _____

Hiking Companions: _____

_____

_____

Distance and Directions to Trailhead: _____

_____

_____

_____

_____

_____

How much time it took to get there: _____

Portalet in parking area: Yes_____ No_____ Seasonal_____

Are dogs allowed: Yes_____ No_____

Trail Length: _____ **Trail Difficulty:** _____

How far I hiked: _____

Time: Hike Started: _____ **Time: Hike Ended:** _____

Time spent hiking: _____

Stopped for lunch: _____

Weather: _____

What I liked best: _____

What I liked least: _____

Camped overnight or longer: _____

_____

What are my goals for this hike?

Insights I had while hiking:

I saw these types of birds, creatures, flowers, insects:

I took photos of:

Was the trail well marked?

Were there many side trails?

More notes about the Trail:

Hike Date: ......

Trail Name: ......

Trail Location: ......

Hiking Companions: ......

......

......

Distance and Directions to Trailhead: ......

......

......

......

......

......

......

How much time it took to get there: ......

Portalet in parking area: Yes ...... **No** ...... **Seasonal** ......

Are dogs allowed: Yes ...... **No** ......

Trail Length: ...... **Trail Difficulty:** ......

How far I hiked: ......

Time: Hike Started: ...... **Time: Hike Ended:** ......

Time spent hiking: ......

Stopped for lunch: ......

Weather: ......

What I liked best: ......

......

What I liked least: ......

......

Camped overnight or longer: ......

......

......

What are my goals for this hike?

Insights I had while hiking:

I saw these types of birds, creatures, flowers, insects:

I took photos of:

Was the trail well marked?

Were there many side trails?

More notes about the Trail:

Hike Date: ....

Trail Name: ....

Trail Location: ....

Hiking Companions: ....

....

....

Distance and Directions to Trailhead: ....

....

....

....

....

....

How much time it took to get there: ....

Portalet in parking area: Yes .... **No** .... **Seasonal** ....

Are dogs allowed: Yes .... **No** ....

Trail Length: .... **Trail Difficulty:** ....

How far I hiked: ....

Time: Hike Started: .... **Time: Hike Ended:** ....

Time spent hiking: ....

Stopped for lunch: ....

....

Weather: ....

What I liked best: ....

....

What I liked least: ....

....

Camped overnight or longer: ....

....

....

What are my goals for this hike?

Insights I had while hiking:

I saw these types of birds, creatures, flowers, insects:

I took photos of:

Was the trail well marked?

Were there many side trails?

More notes about the Trail:

Hike Date: _____

Trail Name: _____

Trail Location: _____

Hiking Companions: _____

_____

_____

Distance and Directions to Trailhead: _____

_____

_____

_____

_____

_____

How much time it took to get there: _____

Portalet in parking area: Yes _____ **No** _____ **Seasonal** _____

Are dogs allowed: Yes _____ **No** _____

Trail Length: _____ **Trail Difficulty:** _____

How far I hiked: _____

Time: Hike Started: _____ **Time: Hike Ended:** _____

Time spent hiking: _____

Stopped for lunch: _____

Weather: _____

What I liked best: _____

What I liked least: _____

Camped overnight or longer: _____

_____

_____

What are my goals for this hike?

Insights I had while hiking:

I saw these types of birds, creatures, flowers, insects:

I took photos of:

Was the trail well marked?

Were there many side trails?

More notes about the Trail:

Hike Date: _____

Trail Name: _____

Trail Location: _____

Hiking Companions: _____

_____

Distance and Directions to Trailhead: _____

_____

_____

_____

_____

_____

How much time it took to get there: _____

Portalet in parking area: Yes ____ No ____ Seasonal _____

Are dogs allowed: Yes ____ No ____

Trail Length: _____ Trail Difficulty: _____

How far I hiked: _____

Time: Hike Started: _____ Time: Hike Ended: _____

Time spent hiking: _____

Stopped for lunch: _____

Weather: _____

What I liked best: _____

What I liked least: _____

Camped overnight or longer: _____

_____

_____

What are my goals for this hike? _____

_____

_____

_____

Insights I had while hiking: _____

_____

_____

_____

_____

_____

I saw these types of birds, creatures, flowers, insects:

_____

_____

_____

I took photos of: _____

_____

_____

_____

_____

_____

Was the trail well marked? _____

Were there many side trails? _____

More notes about the Trail: _____

_____

_____

_____

_____

_____

_____

Hike Date: ....

Trail Name: ....

Trail Location: ....

Hiking Companions: ....

....

Distance and Directions to Trailhead: ....

....

....

....

....

....

....

How much time it took to get there: ....

Portalet in parking area: Yes .... **No** .... **Seasonal** ....

Are dogs allowed: Yes .... **No** ....

Trail Length: .... **Trail Difficulty:** ....

How far I hiked: ....

Time: Hike Started: .... **Time: Hike Ended:** ....

Time spent hiking: ....

Stopped for lunch: ....

Weather: ....

What I liked best: ....

What I liked least: ....

Camped overnight or longer: ....

....

....

What are my goals for this hike?

Insights I had while hiking:

I saw these types of birds, creatures, flowers, insects:

I took photos of:

Was the trail well marked?

Were there many side trails?

More notes about the Trail:

Hike Date: _____

Trail Name: _____

Trail Location: _____

Hiking Companions: _____

_____

Distance and Directions to Trailhead: _____

_____

_____

_____

_____

_____

How much time it took to get there: _____

Portalet in parking area: Yes _____ **No** _____ **Seasonal** _____

Are dogs allowed: Yes _____ **No** _____

Trail Length: _____ **Trail Difficulty:** _____

How far I hiked: _____

Time: Hike Started: _____ **Time: Hike Ended:** _____

Time spent hiking: _____

Stopped for lunch: _____

Weather: _____

What I liked best: _____

What I liked least: _____

Camped overnight or longer: _____

_____

_____

What are my goals for this hike?

Insights I had while hiking:

I saw these types of birds, creatures, flowers, insects:

I took photos of:

Was the trail well marked?

Were there many side trails?

More notes about the Trail:

Describe Your Most Memorable Hiking Experiences.

What insights has hiking given you?

Hike Date: _____

Trail Name: _____

Trail Location: _____

Hiking Companions: _____

_____

Distance and Directions to Trailhead: _____

_____

_____

_____

_____

_____

How much time it took to get there: _____

Portalet in parking area: Yes _____ **No** _____ **Seasonal** _____

Are dogs allowed: Yes _____ **No** _____

Trail Length: _____ **Trail Difficulty:** _____

How far I hiked: _____

Time: Hike Started: _____ **Time: Hike Ended:** _____

Time spent hiking: _____

Stopped for lunch: _____

Weather: _____

What I liked best: _____

_____

What I liked least: _____

_____

Camped overnight or longer: _____

_____

_____

What are my goals for this hike?

Insights I had while hiking:

I saw these types of birds, creatures, flowers, insects:

I took photos of:

Was the trail well marked?

Were there many side trails?

More notes about the Trail:

Hike Date: _____

Trail Name: _____

Trail Location: _____

Hiking Companions: _____

_____

Distance and Directions to Trailhead: _____

_____

_____

_____

_____

_____

How much time it took to get there: _____

Portalet in parking area: Yes _____ **No** _____ **Seasonal** _____

Are dogs allowed: Yes _____ **No** _____

Trail Length: _____ **Trail Difficulty:** _____

How far I hiked: _____

Time: Hike Started: _____ **Time: Hike Ended:** _____

Time spent hiking: _____

Stopped for lunch: _____

Weather: _____

What I liked best: _____

_____

What I liked least: _____

_____

Camped overnight or longer: _____

_____

_____

What are my goals for this hike?

Insights I had while hiking:

I saw these types of birds, creatures, flowers, insects:

I took photos of:

Was the trail well marked?

Were there many side trails?

More notes about the Trail:

Hike Date: ....

Trail Name: ....

Trail Location: ....

Hiking Companions: ....

....

Distance and Directions to Trailhead: ....

....

....

....

....

....

How much time it took to get there: ....

Portalet in parking area: Yes .... **No** .... **Seasonal** ....

Are dogs allowed: Yes .... **No** ....

Trail Length: .... **Trail Difficulty:** ....

How far I hiked: ....

Time: Hike Started: .... **Time: Hike Ended:** ....

Time spent hiking: ....

Stopped for lunch: ....

Weather: ....

What I liked best: ....

....

What I liked least: ....

....

Camped overnight or longer: ....

....

....

What are my goals for this hike?

Insights I had while hiking:

I saw these types of birds, creatures, flowers, insects:

I took photos of:

Was the trail well marked?

Were there many side trails?

More notes about the Trail:

Hike Date: _____

Trail Name: _____

Trail Location: _____

Hiking Companions: _____

_____

Distance and Directions to Trailhead: _____

_____

_____

_____

_____

_____

How much time it took to get there: _____

Portalet in parking area: Yes ____ **No** ____ **Seasonal** _____

Are dogs allowed: Yes ____ **No** ____

Trail Length: _____ **Trail Difficulty:** _____

How far I hiked: _____

Time: Hike Started: _____ **Time: Hike Ended:** _____

Time spent hiking: _____

Stopped for lunch: _____

Weather: _____

What I liked best: _____

What I liked least: _____

Camped overnight or longer: _____

_____

_____

What are my goals for this hike? ....

....

....

Insights I had while hiking: ....

....

....

....

....

I saw these types of birds, creatures, flowers, insects:

....

....

....

I took photos of: ....

....

....

....

....

....

Was the trail well marked? ....

Were there many side trails? ....

More notes about the Trail: ....

....

....

....

....

....

....

....

Hike Date: _____

Trail Name: _____

Trail Location: _____

Hiking Companions: _____

_____

Distance and Directions to Trailhead: _____

_____

_____

_____

_____

_____

How much time it took to get there: _____

Portalet in parking area: Yes _____ No _____ Seasonal _____

Are dogs allowed: Yes _____ No _____

Trail Length: _____ Trail Difficulty: _____

How far I hiked: _____

Time: Hike Started: _____ Time: Hike Ended: _____

Time spent hiking: _____

Stopped for lunch: _____

Weather: _____

What I liked best: _____

What I liked least: _____

Camped overnight or longer: _____

_____

_____

What are my goals for this hike? _____

_____
_____
_____

Insights I had while hiking: _____

_____
_____
_____
_____
_____

I saw these types of birds, creatures, flowers, insects:

_____
_____
_____

I took photos of: _____

_____
_____
_____
_____

Was the trail well marked? _____

Were there many side trails? _____

More notes about the Trail: _____

_____
_____
_____
_____
_____
_____
_____

Hike Date: _____

Trail Name: _____

Trail Location: _____

Hiking Companions: _____

_____

Distance and Directions to Trailhead: _____

_____

_____

_____

_____

_____

How much time it took to get there: _____

Portalet in parking area: Yes _____ **No** _____ **Seasonal** _____

Are dogs allowed: Yes _____ **No** _____

Trail Length: _____ **Trail Difficulty:** _____

How far I hiked: _____

Time: Hike Started: _____ **Time: Hike Ended:** _____

Time spent hiking: _____

Stopped for lunch: _____

Weather: _____

What I liked best: _____

_____

What I liked least: _____

_____

Camped overnight or longer: _____

_____

_____

What are my goals for this hike?

Insights I had while hiking:

I saw these types of birds, creatures, flowers, insects:

I took photos of:

Was the trail well marked?

Were there many side trails?

More notes about the Trail:

Describe Your Most Memorable Hiking Experiences.

What insights has hiking given you?

Hike Date: _____

Trail Name: _____

Trail Location: _____

Hiking Companions: _____

_____

Distance and Directions to Trailhead: _____

_____

_____

_____

_____

_____

How much time it took to get there: _____

Portalet in parking area: Yes _____ **No** _____ **Seasonal** _____

Are dogs allowed: Yes _____ **No** _____

Trail Length: _____ **Trail Difficulty:** _____

How far I hiked: _____

Time: Hike Started: _____ **Time: Hike Ended:** _____

Time spent hiking: _____

Stopped for lunch: _____

Weather: _____

What I liked best: _____

What I liked least: _____

Camped overnight or longer: _____

_____

_____

What are my goals for this hike?

Insights I had while hiking:

I saw these types of birds, creatures, flowers, insects:

I took photos of:

Was the trail well marked?

Were there many side trails?

More notes about the Trail:

Hike Date: _____

Trail Name: _____

Trail Location: _____

Hiking Companions: _____

_____

Distance and Directions to Trailhead: _____

_____

_____

_____

_____

_____

How much time it took to get there: _____

Portalet in parking area: Yes ____ **No** ____ **Seasonal** ____

Are dogs allowed: Yes ____ **No** ____

Trail Length: ____ **Trail Difficulty:** ____

How far I hiked: _____

Time: Hike Started: ____ **Time: Hike Ended:** ____

Time spent hiking: _____

Stopped for lunch: _____

Weather: _____

What I liked best: _____

_____

What I liked least: _____

_____

Camped overnight or longer: _____

_____

_____

What are my goals for this hike? _____

_____

_____

_____

Insights I had while hiking: _____

_____

_____

_____

_____

_____

I saw these types of birds, creatures, flowers, insects: ____

_____

_____

_____

I took photos of: _____

_____

_____

_____

_____

Was the trail well marked? _____

Were there many side trails? _____

More notes about the Trail: _____

_____

_____

_____

_____

_____

_____

_____

Hike Date: ....

Trail Name: _____

Trail Location: _____

Hiking Companions: _____

_____

_____

Distance and Directions to Trailhead: _____

_____

_____

_____

_____

_____

_____

How much time it took to get there: _____

Portalet in parking area: Yes _____ **No** _____ **Seasonal** _____

Are dogs allowed: Yes _____ **No** _____

Trail Length: _____ **Trail Difficulty:** _____

How far I hiked: _____

Time: Hike Started: _____ **Time: Hike Ended:** _____

Time spent hiking: _____

Stopped for lunch: _____

_____

Weather: _____

What I liked best: _____

_____

What I liked least: _____

_____

Camped overnight or longer: _____

_____

_____

_____

What are my goals for this hike?

Insights I had while hiking:

I saw these types of birds, creatures, flowers, insects:

I took photos of:

Was the trail well marked?

Were there many side trails?

More notes about the Trail:

Hike Date: _____

Trail Name: _____

Trail Location: _____

Hiking Companions: _____

_____

_____

Distance and Directions to Trailhead: _____

_____

_____

_____

_____

_____

_____

How much time it took to get there: _____

Portalet in parking area: Yes ____ **No** ____ **Seasonal** _____

Are dogs allowed: Yes ____ **No** _____

Trail Length: _____ **Trail Difficulty:** _____

How far I hiked: _____

Time: Hike Started: _____ **Time: Hike Ended:** _____

Time spent hiking: _____

Stopped for lunch: _____

Weather: _____

What I liked best: _____

What I liked least: _____

Camped overnight or longer: _____

_____

_____

_____

What are my goals for this hike?

Insights I had while hiking:

I saw these types of birds, creatures, flowers, insects:

I took photos of:

Was the trail well marked?

Were there many side trails?

More notes about the Trail:

Hike Date:

Trail Name:

Trail Location:

Hiking Companions:

Distance and Directions to Trailhead:

How much time it took to get there:

Portalet in parking area: Yes___ No___ Seasonal___

Are dogs allowed: Yes___ No___

Trail Length:___ Trail Difficulty:___

How far I hiked:

Time: Hike Started:___ Time: Hike Ended:___

Time spent hiking:

Stopped for lunch:

Weather:

What I liked best:

What I liked least:

Camped overnight or longer:

What are my goals for this hike? _____

_____

_____

_____

Insights I had while hiking: _____

_____

_____

_____

_____

_____

I saw these types of birds, creatures, flowers, insects: _____

_____

_____

_____

I took photos of: _____

_____

_____

_____

_____

_____

Was the trail well marked? _____

Were there many side trails? _____

More notes about the Trail: _____

_____

_____

_____

_____

_____

_____

Hike Date: _____

Trail Name: _____

Trail Location: _____

Hiking Companions: _____

_____

Distance and Directions to Trailhead: _____

_____

_____

_____

_____

_____

_____

How much time it took to get there: _____

Portalet in parking area: Yes ____ No ____ Seasonal ____

Are dogs allowed: Yes ____ No ____

Trail Length: _____ **Trail Difficulty:** _____

How far I hiked: _____

Time: Hike Started: _____ **Time: Hike Ended:** _____

Time spent hiking: _____

Stopped for lunch: _____

Weather: _____

What I liked best: _____

_____

What I liked least: _____

_____

Camped overnight or longer: _____

_____

_____

What are my goals for this hike?

Insights I had while hiking:

I saw these types of birds, creatures, flowers, insects:

I took photos of:

Was the trail well marked?

Were there many side trails?

More notes about the Trail:

Hike Date: _____

Trail Name: _____

Trail Location: _____

Hiking Companions: _____

_____

_____

Distance and Directions to Trailhead: _____

_____

_____

_____

_____

_____

How much time it took to get there: _____

Portalet in parking area: Yes ____ No ____ Seasonal _____

Are dogs allowed: Yes ____ No _____

Trail Length: _____ **Trail Difficulty:** _____

How far I hiked: _____

Time: Hike Started: _____ **Time: Hike Ended:** _____

Time spent hiking: _____

Stopped for lunch: _____

Weather: _____

What I liked best: _____

_____

What I liked least: _____

_____

Camped overnight or longer: _____

_____

_____

What are my goals for this hike?

Insights I had while hiking:

I saw these types of birds, creatures, flowers, insects:

I took photos of:

Was the trail well marked?

Were there many side trails?

More notes about the Trail:

Describe Your Most Memorable Hiking Experiences.

What insights has hiking given you?

Hike Date:_____

Trail Name:_____

Trail Location:_____

Hiking Companions:_____

_____

_____

Distance and Directions to Trailhead:_____

_____

_____

_____

_____

_____

_____

How much time it took to get there:_____

Portalet in parking area: Yes____ **No**____ **Seasonal**_____

Are dogs allowed: Yes____ **No**____

Trail Length:_____ **Trail Difficulty:**_____

How far I hiked:_____

Time: Hike Started:_____ **Time: Hike Ended:**_____

Time spent hiking:_____

Stopped for lunch:_____

Weather:_____

What I liked best:_____

_____

What I liked least:_____

_____

Camped overnight or longer:_____

_____

_____

_____

What are my goals for this hike? _____

_____

_____

_____

Insights I had while hiking: _____

_____

_____

_____

_____

_____

I saw these types of birds, creatures, flowers, insects:

_____

_____

_____

I took photos of: _____

_____

_____

_____

_____

_____

Was the trail well marked? _____

Were there many side trails? _____

More notes about the Trail: _____

_____

_____

_____

_____

_____

_____

_____

Hike Date: _____

Trail Name: _____

Trail Location: _____

Hiking Companions: _____

_____

_____

Distance and Directions to Trailhead: _____

_____

_____

_____

_____

_____

_____

How much time it took to get there: _____

Portalet in parking area: Yes _____ **No** _____ **Seasonal** _____

Are dogs allowed: Yes _____ **No** _____

Trail Length: _____ **Trail Difficulty:** _____

How far I hiked: _____

Time: Hike Started: _____ **Time: Hike Ended:** _____

Time spent hiking: _____

Stopped for lunch: _____

Weather: _____

What I liked best: _____

_____

What I liked least: _____

_____

Camped overnight or longer: _____

_____

_____

What are my goals for this hike?

Insights I had while hiking:

I saw these types of birds, creatures, flowers, insects:

I took photos of:

Was the trail well marked?

Were there many side trails?

More notes about the Trail:

Hike Date: ....

Trail Name: ....

Trail Location: ....

Hiking Companions: ....

....

....

Distance and Directions to Trailhead: ....

....

....

....

....

....

How much time it took to get there: ....

Portalet in parking area: Yes ...... **No** ...... **Seasonal** ....

Are dogs allowed: Yes ...... **No** ......

Trail Length: .... **Trail Difficulty:** ....

How far I hiked: ....

Time: Hike Started: .... **Time: Hike Ended:** ....

Time spent hiking: ....

Stopped for lunch: ....

Weather: ....

What I liked best: ....

What I liked least: ....

Camped overnight or longer: ....

....

....

What are my goals for this hike?

Insights I had while hiking:

I saw these types of birds, creatures, flowers, insects:

I took photos of:

Was the trail well marked?

Were there many side trails?

More notes about the Trail:

Hike Date: ....

Trail Name: ....

Trail Location: ....

Hiking Companions: ....

....

....

Distance and Directions to Trailhead: ....

....

....

....

....

....

How much time it took to get there: ....

Portalet in parking area: Yes .... **No** .... **Seasonal** ....

Are dogs allowed: Yes .... **No** ....

Trail Length: .... **Trail Difficulty:** ....

How far I hiked: ....

Time: Hike Started: .... **Time: Hike Ended:** ....

Time spent hiking: ....

Stopped for lunch: ....

Weather: ....

What I liked best: ....

....

What I liked least: ....

....

Camped overnight or longer: ....

....

....

....

What are my goals for this hike?

Insights I had while hiking:

I saw these types of birds, creatures, flowers, insects:

I took photos of:

Was the trail well marked?

Were there many side trails?

More notes about the Trail:

Hike Date: _____

Trail Name: _____

Trail Location: _____

Hiking Companions: _____

_____

_____

Distance and Directions to Trailhead: _____

_____

_____

_____

_____

_____

How much time it took to get there: _____

Portalet in parking area: Yes _____ No _____ Seasonal _____

Are dogs allowed: Yes _____ No _____

Trail Length: _____ **Trail Difficulty:** _____

How far I hiked: _____

Time: Hike Started: _____ **Time: Hike Ended:** _____

Time spent hiking: _____

Stopped for lunch: _____

Weather: _____

What I liked best: _____

_____

What I liked least: _____

_____

Camped overnight or longer: _____

_____

_____

_____

What are my goals for this hike?

Insights I had while hiking:

I saw these types of birds, creatures, flowers, insects:

I took photos of:

Was the trail well marked?

Were there many side trails?

More notes about the Trail:

Hike Date: _____

Trail Name: _____

Trail Location: _____

Hiking Companions: _____

_____

Distance and Directions to Trailhead: _____

_____

_____

_____

_____

_____

How much time it took to get there: _____

Portalet in parking area: Yes _____ **No** _____ **Seasonal** _____

Are dogs allowed: Yes _____ **No** _____

Trail Length: _____ **Trail Difficulty:** _____

How far I hiked: _____

Time: Hike Started: _____ **Time: Hike Ended:** _____

Time spent hiking: _____

Stopped for lunch: _____

Weather: _____

What I liked best: _____

_____

What I liked least: _____

_____

Camped overnight or longer: _____

_____

_____

_____

What are my goals for this hike?

Insights I had while hiking:

I saw these types of birds, creatures, flowers, insects:

I took photos of:

Was the trail well marked?

Were there many side trails?

More notes about the Trail:

Describe Your Most Memorable Hiking Experiences.

What insights has hiking given you?

Hike Date: _____

Trail Name: _____

Trail Location: _____

Hiking Companions: _____

_____

_____

Distance and Directions to Trailhead: _____

_____

_____

_____

_____

_____

How much time it took to get there: _____

Portalet in parking area: Yes _____ **No** _____ **Seasonal** _____

Are dogs allowed: Yes _____ **No** _____

Trail Length: _____ **Trail Difficulty:** _____

How far I hiked: _____

Time: Hike Started: _____ **Time: Hike Ended:** _____

Time spent hiking: _____

Stopped for lunch: _____

Weather: _____

What I liked best: _____

_____

What I liked least: _____

_____

Camped overnight or longer: _____

_____

_____

What are my goals for this hike? _____

_____

_____

_____

Insights I had while hiking: _____

_____

_____

_____

_____

_____

I saw these types of birds, creatures, flowers, insects:

_____

_____

_____

I took photos of: _____

_____

_____

_____

_____

_____

Was the trail well marked? _____

Were there many side trails? _____

More notes about the Trail: _____

_____

_____

_____

_____

_____

_____

_____

Hike Date: _____

Trail Name: _____

Trail Location: _____

Hiking Companions: _____

_____

_____

Distance and Directions to Trailhead: _____

_____

_____

_____

_____

_____

How much time it took to get there: _____

Portalet in parking area: Yes _____ No _____ Seasonal _____

Are dogs allowed: Yes _____ No _____

Trail Length: _____ **Trail Difficulty:** _____

How far I hiked: _____

Time: Hike Started: _____ **Time: Hike Ended:** _____

Time spent hiking: _____

Stopped for lunch: _____

Weather: _____

What I liked best: _____

_____

What I liked least: _____

_____

Camped overnight or longer: _____

_____

_____

What are my goals for this hike?

_____

Insights I had while hiking:

_____

I saw these types of birds, creatures, flowers, insects:

_____

I took photos of:

_____

Was the trail well marked?

Were there many side trails?

More notes about the Trail:

_____

Hike Date:

Trail Name:

Trail Location:

Hiking Companions:

Distance and Directions to Trailhead:

How much time it took to get there:

Portalet in parking area: Yes ___ No ___ Seasonal ___

Are dogs allowed: Yes ___ No ___

Trail Length: ___ Trail Difficulty: ___

How far I hiked:

Time: Hike Started: ___ Time: Hike Ended: ___

Time spent hiking:

Stopped for lunch:

Weather:

What I liked best:

What I liked least:

Camped overnight or longer:

What are my goals for this hike?

Insights I had while hiking:

I saw these types of birds, creatures, flowers, insects:

I took photos of:

Was the trail well marked?

Were there many side trails?

More notes about the Trail:

Hike Date:_____

Trail Name: _____

Trail Location: _____

Hiking Companions: _____

_____

_____

Distance and Directions to Trailhead: _____

_____

_____

_____

_____

_____

_____

How much time it took to get there: _____

Portalet in parking area: Yes____ No____ Seasonal_____

Are dogs allowed: Yes____ No____

Trail Length: _____ **Trail Difficulty:** _____

How far I hiked: _____

Time: Hike Started: _____ **Time: Hike Ended:** _____

Time spent hiking: _____

Stopped for lunch: _____

Weather: _____

What I liked best: _____

_____

What I liked least: _____

_____

Camped overnight or longer: _____

_____

_____

_____

What are my goals for this hike?

Insights I had while hiking:

I saw these types of birds, creatures, flowers, insects:

I took photos of:

Was the trail well marked?

Were there many side trails?

More notes about the Trail:

Hike Date: _____

Trail Name: _____

Trail Location: _____

Hiking Companions: _____
_____

Distance and Directions to Trailhead: _____
_____
_____
_____
_____
_____

How much time it took to get there: _____

Portalet in parking area: Yes _____ No _____ Seasonal _____

Are dogs allowed: Yes _____ No _____

Trail Length: _____ **Trail Difficulty:** _____

How far I hiked: _____

Time: Hike Started: _____ **Time: Hike Ended:** _____

Time spent hiking: _____

Stopped for lunch: _____

Weather: _____

What I liked best: _____
_____

What I liked least: _____
_____

Camped overnight or longer: _____
_____
_____

What are my goals for this hike?

Insights I had while hiking:

I saw these types of birds, creatures, flowers, insects:

I took photos of:

Was the trail well marked?

Were there many side trails?

More notes about the Trail:

Hike Date: _____

Trail Name: _____

Trail Location: _____

Hiking Companions: _____

_____

Distance and Directions to Trailhead: _____

_____

_____

_____

_____

_____

How much time it took to get there: _____

Portalet in parking area: Yes ____ **No** ____ **Seasonal** _____

Are dogs allowed: Yes ____ **No** ____

Trail Length: _____ **Trail Difficulty:** _____

How far I hiked: _____

Time: Hike Started: _____ **Time: Hike Ended:** _____

Time spent hiking: _____

Stopped for lunch: _____

Weather: _____

What I liked best: _____

_____

What I liked least: _____

_____

Camped overnight or longer: _____

_____

_____

What are my goals for this hike?

Insights I had while hiking:

I saw these types of birds, creatures, flowers, insects:

I took photos of:

Was the trail well marked?

Were there many side trails?

More notes about the Trail:

Hike Date: _____

Trail Name: _____

Trail Location: _____

Hiking Companions: _____

_____

_____

Distance and Directions to Trailhead: _____

_____

_____

_____

_____

_____

_____

How much time it took to get there: _____

Portalet in parking area: Yes _____ No _____ Seasonal _____

Are dogs allowed: Yes _____ No _____

Trail Length: _____ **Trail Difficulty:** _____

How far I hiked: _____

Time: Hike Started: _____ **Time: Hike Ended:** _____

Time spent hiking: _____

Stopped for lunch: _____

_____

Weather: _____

What I liked best: _____

_____

What I liked least: _____

_____

Camped overnight or longer: _____

_____

_____

_____

What are my goals for this hike?

Insights I had while hiking:

I saw these types of birds, creatures, flowers, insects:

I took photos of:

Was the trail well marked?

Were there many side trails?

More notes about the Trail:

Describe Your Most Memorable Hiking Experiences.

What insights has hiking given you?

Hike Date: _____

Trail Name: _____

Trail Location: _____

Hiking Companions: _____

_____

_____

Distance and Directions to Trailhead: _____

_____

_____

_____

_____

_____

How much time it took to get there: _____

Portalet in parking area: Yes _____ **No** _____ **Seasonal** _____

Are dogs allowed: Yes _____ **No** _____

Trail Length: _____ **Trail Difficulty:** _____

How far I hiked: _____

Time: Hike Started: _____ **Time: Hike Ended:** _____

Time spent hiking: _____

Stopped for lunch: _____

Weather: _____

What I liked best: _____

_____

What I liked least: _____

_____

Camped overnight or longer: _____

_____

_____

What are my goals for this hike?

Insights I had while hiking:

I saw these types of birds, creatures, flowers, insects:

I took photos of:

Was the trail well marked?

Were there many side trails?

More notes about the Trail:

Hike Date: _____

Trail Name: _____

Trail Location: _____

Hiking Companions: _____

_____

Distance and Directions to Trailhead: _____

_____

_____

_____

_____

_____

_____

How much time it took to get there: _____

Portalet in parking area: Yes ____ **No** ____ **Seasonal** _____

Are dogs allowed: Yes ____ **No** ____

Trail Length: _____ **Trail Difficulty:** _____

How far I hiked: _____

Time: Hike Started: _____ **Time: Hike Ended:** _____

Time spent hiking: _____

Stopped for lunch: _____

Weather: _____

What I liked best: _____

_____

What I liked least: _____

_____

Camped overnight or longer: _____

_____

_____

_____

What are my goals for this hike?

Insights I had while hiking:

I saw these types of birds, creatures, flowers, insects:

I took photos of:

Was the trail well marked?

Were there many side trails?

More notes about the Trail:

Hike Date: _____

Trail Name: _____

Trail Location: _____

Hiking Companions: _____

_____

_____

Distance and Directions to Trailhead: _____

_____

_____

_____

_____

_____

How much time it took to get there: _____

Portalet in parking area: Yes_____ No_____ Seasonal_____

Are dogs allowed: Yes_____ No_____

Trail Length: _____ **Trail Difficulty:** _____

How far I hiked: _____

Time: Hike Started: _____ **Time: Hike Ended:** _____

Time spent hiking: _____

Stopped for lunch: _____

Weather: _____

What I liked best: _____

What I liked least: _____

Camped overnight or longer: _____

_____

_____

What are my goals for this hike? _____
_____
_____
_____

Insights I had while hiking: _____
_____
_____
_____
_____
_____

I saw these types of birds, creatures, flowers, insects:
_____
_____

I took photos of: _____
_____
_____
_____
_____

Was the trail well marked? _____
Were there many side trails? _____
More notes about the Trail: _____
_____
_____
_____
_____
_____
_____
_____

Hike Date: _____

Trail Name: _____

Trail Location: _____

Hiking Companions: _____

_____

_____

Distance and Directions to Trailhead: _____

_____

_____

_____

_____

_____

_____

How much time it took to get there: _____

Portalet in parking area: Yes _____ **No** _____ **Seasonal** _____

Are dogs allowed: Yes _____ **No** _____

Trail Length: _____ **Trail Difficulty:** _____

How far I hiked: _____

Time: Hike Started: _____ **Time: Hike Ended:** _____

Time spent hiking: _____

Stopped for lunch: _____

Weather: _____

What I liked best: _____

_____

What I liked least: _____

_____

Camped overnight or longer: _____

_____

_____

What are my goals for this hike?

Insights I had while hiking:

I saw these types of birds, creatures, flowers, insects:

I took photos of:

Was the trail well marked?

Were there many side trails?

More notes about the Trail:

Hike Date: _____

Trail Name: _____

Trail Location: _____

Hiking Companions: _____

_____

_____

Distance and Directions to Trailhead: _____

_____

_____

_____

_____

_____

_____

How much time it took to get there: _____

Portalet in parking area: Yes _____ No _____ Seasonal _____

Are dogs allowed: Yes _____ No _____

Trail Length: _____ **Trail Difficulty:** _____

How far I hiked: _____

Time: Hike Started: _____ **Time: Hike Ended:** _____

Time spent hiking: _____

Stopped for lunch: _____

_____

Weather: _____

What I liked best: _____

_____

What I liked least: _____

_____

Camped overnight or longer: _____

_____

_____

_____

What are my goals for this hike? _____

_____

_____

_____

Insights I had while hiking: _____

_____

_____

_____

_____

_____

I saw these types of birds, creatures, flowers, insects:

_____

_____

_____

I took photos of: _____

_____

_____

_____

_____

_____

Was the trail well marked? _____

Were there many side trails? _____

More notes about the Trail: _____

_____

_____

_____

_____

_____

_____

Hike Date: _____

Trail Name: _____

Trail Location: _____

Hiking Companions: _____

_____

Distance and Directions to Trailhead: _____

_____

_____

_____

_____

_____

_____

How much time it took to get there: _____

Portalet in parking area: Yes _____ **No** _____ **Seasonal** _____

Are dogs allowed: Yes _____ **No** _____

Trail Length: _____ **Trail Difficulty:** _____

How far I hiked: _____

Time: Hike Started: _____ **Time: Hike Ended:** _____

Time spent hiking: _____

Stopped for lunch: _____

Weather: _____

What I liked best: _____

_____

What I liked least: _____

_____

Camped overnight or longer: _____

_____

_____

What are my goals for this hike?

Insights I had while hiking:

I saw these types of birds, creatures, flowers, insects:

I took photos of:

Was the trail well marked?

Were there many side trails?

More notes about the Trail:

Describe Your Most Memorable Hiking Experiences.

What insights has hiking given you?

Earth, Teach Me

Earth teach me quiet ~ as the grasses are still with new light.
Earth teach me suffering ~ as old stones suffer with memory.
Earth teach me humility ~ as blossoms are humble with beginning.
Earth teach me caring ~ as mothers nurture their young.
Earth teach me courage ~ as the tree that stands alone.
Earth teach me limitation ~ as the ant that crawls on the ground.
Earth teach me freedom ~ as the eagle that soars in the sky.
Earth teach me acceptance ~ as the leaves that die each fall.
Earth teach me renewal ~ as the seed that rises in the spring.
Earth teach me to forget myself ~ as melted snow forgets its life.
Earth teach me to remember kindness ~ as dry fields weep with rain.
~ Ute Prayer ~

A Little History about the Origin of Hiking from Around the World.

During the 18th-century, the idea of taking a walk in the countryside for pleasure developed because of changing attitudes to the landscape and nature, associated with the Romantic movement. Before this time, walking generally indicated poverty and was also associated with vagrancy.

Thomas West, an English priest, popularized the idea of walking for pleasure in his guide to the Lake District of 1778. He wrote in the introduction that he aimed "to encourage the taste of visiting the lakes by furnishing the traveller with a Guide; and for that purpose, the writer has here collected and laid before him, all the select stations and points of view, noticed by those authors who have last made the tour of the lakes, verified by his own repeated observations."

Soon thereafter, many people in a higher life situation began to enjoy viewing the world around them by focusing on their aesthetic qualities and walking became a past time also enjoyed by the elite. Now hiking is enjoyed around the world by people of every class that enjoy experiencing the beauty of the natural world that surrounds them.

There are many countries that define hiking as *"walking outdoors on a trail, for recreational purposes."*

Hiking is very popular in the United States, Canada, Ireland, New Zealand, Australia and United Kingdom. The term *"walk-about"* is a more common term than hiking in Australia. The Australian term *"bushwalking"* refers to both on and off-trail hiking. New Zealanders use the terms *"tramping" (particularly for overnight and longer trips)*, *"walking"* or *"bushwalking"* more often than hiking. Hiking a long-distance trail from end-to-end is also referred to as *"trekking"* in some places. Multi-day hiking in the mountainous regions of India, Pakistan, Nepal, North America, South America, Iran and in the highlands of East Africa is referred to as *"trekking"* when describing hiking there. In North America, multi-day hikes, that usually involve camping, are referred to as *"backpacking"* trips. In the United Kingdom, the word *"walking"* is also commonly used, as well as *"rambling"*, while walking in mountainous areas is called *"hillwalking"*.

Sometimes people find themselves off a well-defined trail and in areas of heavy brush or thick forest areas. This involves a bit of very challenging walking through dense forest, undergrowth, or bushes. This usually means they will be *"bushwhacking"*. Moving foward in this type of situation requires moving branches and other types of vegetation aside or pushing your way through very tall plants. In extreme cases where the vegetation is extremely dense and impedes a person being able to move forward, a machete may be needed to clear a pathway. It is always best to avoid this type of situation and stay on a well-defined trail.

A Place I Envision Hiking

This would be a local/vacation/camping adventure.

Name of Trail:

Location:

How I will travel there:

Why do I want to do this hike?

What I have researched about this future hike:

A Place I Envision Hiking

This would be a local/vacation/camping adventure.

Name of Trail:

Location:

How I will travel there:

Why do I want to do this hike?

What I have researched about this future hike:

A Place I Envision Hiking

This would be a local/vacation/camping adventure.

Name of Trail: _____

Location: _____

_____

How I will travel there: _____

_____

_____

Why do I want to do this hike?

_____

_____

_____

_____

What I have researched about this future hike:

_____

_____

_____

_____

_____

_____

_____

_____

_____

_____

_____

_____

A Place I Envision Hiking

This would be a local/vacation/camping adventure.

Name of Trail:

Location:

How I will travel there:

Why do I want to do this hike?

What I have researched about this future hike:

A Place I Envision Hiking

This would be a local/vacation/camping adventure.

Name of Trail: ....

Location: ....

....

How I will travel there: ....

....

....

Why do I want to do this hike?

....

....

....

....

What I have researched about this future hike:

....

....

....

....

....

....

....

....

....

....

....

A Place I Envision Hiking

This would be a local/vacation/camping adventure.

Name of Trail:

Location:

How I will travel there:

Why do I want to do this hike?

What I have researched about this future hike:

A Place I Envision Hiking

This would be a local/vacation/camping adventure.

Name of Trail: _____

Location: _____

_____

How I will travel there: _____

_____

_____

Why do I want to do this hike?

_____

_____

_____

_____

_____

What I have researched about this future hike:

_____

_____

_____

_____

_____

_____

_____

_____

_____

_____

_____

_____

A Place I Envision Hiking

This would be a local/vacation/camping adventure.

Name of Trail: _____

Location: _____

_____

How I will travel there: _____

_____

_____

Why do I want to do this hike?

_____

_____

_____

_____

What I have researched about this future hike:

_____

_____

_____

_____

_____

_____

_____

_____

_____

_____

Trail Name and Page # With Information About My Hikes

Trail Name and Page # With Information About My Hikes

The moment one gives close attention to anything,
even a blade of grass, it becomes a mysterious, awesome,
indescribably magnificent world in itself.
~ Henry Miller ~

It is good to have an end to journey toward;
but it is the journey that matters in the end.
~ Ursula K. Le Guin ~

If you haven't already downloaded your free bonus *"Tips for Hiking Safely"*, do it NOW!

Sign up to download:
My Hiking Journal Bonus Tips for Hiking Safely at:

www.hierographicsbooksllc.com/hiking-journal-safely/

These tips are designed to help you take the right steps on a path to safely experience your hiking adventures in Nature.

THANK YOU!
FOR PURCHASING THIS HIKING JOURNAL.
HIKING AND ACKNOWLEDGING THE PLEASURABLE THINGS IN YOUR WORLD IS THE BEST WAY TO CREATE AND ENJOY A HEALTHY AND JOYFUL LIFE.

Made in the USA
Columbia, SC
06 August 2017